the unsinkable charlie brown

Books by Charles M. Schulz

Peanuts
More Peanuts
Good Grief, More Peanuts!
Good Ol' Charlie Brown
Snoopy
You're Out of Your Mind, Charlie Brown!
But We Love You, Charlie Brown
Peanuts Revisited
Go Fly a Kite, Charlie Brown
Peanuts Every Sunday
It's a Dog's Life, Charlie Brown
You Can't Win, Charlie Brown
Snoopy, Come Home
You Can Do It, Charlie Brown
We're Right Behind You, Charlie Brown
As You Like It, Charlie Brown
Sunday's Fun Day, Charlie Brown
You Need Help, Charlie Brown
Snoopy and The Red Baron
The Unsinkable Charlie Brown

the unsinkable charlie brown

A NEW **PEANUTS** BOOK
BY CHARLES M. SCHULZ

HOLT, RINEHART AND WINSTON
New York • Chicago • San Francisco

NEXT YEAR I'M GOING TO BE A CHANGED PERSON!

THAT'S A LAUGH, CHARLIE BROWN

I MEAN IT! I'M GOING TO BE STRONG AND FIRM..

FORGET IT..YOU'LL ALWAYS BE WISHY-WASHY!

WHY CAN'T I CHANGE JUST A LITTLE BIT?

I'LL BE WISHY ONE DAY AND WASHY THE NEXT!

HOW CAN YOU BE HAPPY WHEN YOU DON'T KNOW WHAT THIS YEAR HAS IN STORE FOR YOU?

DON'T YOU WORRY ABOUT ALL THE THINGS THAT CAN HAPPEN?

THAT'S BETTER...LIVE IN DREAD AND FEAR... BE SENSIBLE...

HE HE HE HE HE HE HE HE

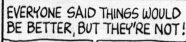

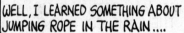
WELL, I LEARNED SOMETHING ABOUT JUMPING ROPE IN THE RAIN....

SOME JUMP ROPES **SHRINK** !

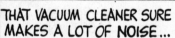
THAT VACUUM CLEANER SURE MAKES A LOT OF NOISE...

YOU'D MAKE A LOT OF NOISE TOO IF SOMEONE WERE PUSHING YOU ACROSS A CARPET ON YOUR FACE!

DEAR EDITOR OF "LETTERS TO THE EDITOR", HOW HAVE YOU BEEN?

"HOW HAVE YOU BEEN?" WHAT SORT OF LETTER IS THAT TO WRITE TO AN EDITOR?

I JUST THOUGHT HE MIGHT APPRECIATE HAVING SOMEONE INQUIRE ABOUT THE STATE OF HIS HEALTH

EDITORS ARE SORT OF HUMAN, TOO, YOU KNOW!

SCHULZ

DOES IT BOTHER YOU TO THINK THAT THERE MAY BE PEOPLE AROUND WHO DISLIKE YOU?

DISLIKE **ME**? HOW COULD ANYONE POSSIBLY DISLIKE **ME**? THERE'S NOTHING TO DISLIKE!

JEALOUS, MAYBE....YES, I COULD UNDERSTAND THAT... I CAN SEE HOW SOMEONE COULD BE JEALOUS OF ME...BUT DISLIKE? NO, THAT'S JUST NOT POSSIBLE...

SO GETTING BACK TO YOUR ORIGINAL QUESTION...

FORGET IT..

SCHULZ

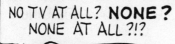

SEE WHAT YOU THINK OF THIS IDEA...

WHY DON'T WE TELL MOM THAT WE'RE SORRY ABOUT ARGUING OVER THE TV ALL THE TIME, AND PROMISE NEVER TO DO IT AGAIN?...THAT WAY, MAYBE SHE'LL FORGIVE US, AND BRING THE TV BACK INTO THE HOUSE..

YOU MEAN, COMPROMISE?

NEVER!

I THINK I'M STUCK WITH A BAD ALLIANCE!

YOU'RE LETTING OUR HAVING NO TV GET YOU DOWN...RELAX! FORGET IT!

HE'S TAKING THIS WHOLE BUSINESS FAR TOO CALMLY...I WONDER IF HE'S SNEAKING OVER TO SOMEONE ELSE'S HOUSE TO WATCH TV....

AH, HA!

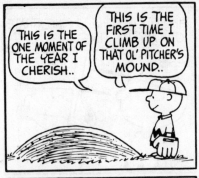

HOW DO THINGS LIKE THIS HAPPEN TO ME?

I'M TOO EASY-GOING, THAT'S WHY! I SHOULD HAVE SAID SOMETHING AS SOON AS THAT STUPID BIRD STARTED TO BUILD THIS NEST...

THE NEXT THING YOU KNOW THERE'LL BE..

I KNEW IT!

cheep?

GOOD GRIEF! WHAT A PREDICAMENT!

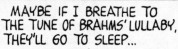

MAYBE IF I BREATHE TO THE TUNE OF BRAHMS' LULLABY, THEY'LL GO TO SLEEP...

I BREATHE A GOOD LULLABY!

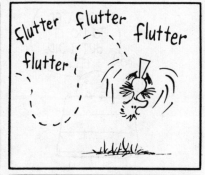

TRY TO STAY CALM....
I HAVE TERRIBLE NEWS!

DAD'S BEEN TRANSFERRED!
WE'RE MOVING TO A NEW CITY!

AAUGH!

THIS MAY BE
MY LAST GAME,
CHARLIE BROWN

MY DAD'S BEEN TRANSFERRED...
WE'RE MOVING TO A NEW CITY...I'LL
PROBABLY NEVER SEE YOU AGAIN...

UNLESS, OF COURSE, WE HAPPEN
TO GO TO THE SAME COLLEGE..
WHAT COLLEGE DO YOU THINK
YOU'LL BE GOING TO?

IT'S KIND OF HARD TO DECIDE IN
THE LAST HALF OF THE NINTH INNING

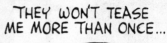

C'MON, LINUS, EACH OF US IS SUPPOSED TO SAY A FEW WORDS AROUND THE CAMPFIRE TONIGHT...

AS I STAND HERE TONIGHT FAR FROM HOME, I AM REMINDED OF THE WORDS FROM JEREMIAH, "KEEP YOUR VOICE FROM WEEPING, AND YOUR EYES FROM TEARS;

FOR YOUR WORK SHALL BE REWARDED, SAYS THE LORD, AND THEY SHALL COME BACK FROM THE LAND OF THE ENEMY. THERE IS HOPE FOR THE FUTURE, SAYS THE LORD, AND YOUR CHILDREN SHALL COME BACK TO THEIR OWN COUNTRY."

INCIDENTALLY, HAVE ANY OF YOU EVER BEEN TOLD ABOUT "THE GREAT PUMPKIN"?

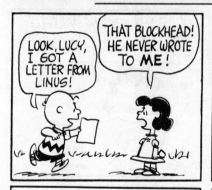

LOOK, LUCY, I GOT A LETTER FROM LINUS!

THAT BLOCKHEAD! HE NEVER WROTE TO ME!

HE SAID HE'S MET ROY, THAT SAME KID I MET LAST YEAR... AND HE SAID HE GAVE A LITTLE TALK AROUND THE CAMPFIRE LAST NIGHT

THAT STUPID BLOCKHEAD

HE SAID HE TOLD ALL THE KIDS ABOUT "THE GREAT PUMPKIN," AND AFTERWARDS THEY ELECTED HIM CAMP PRESIDENT!

HE SAID HE'S GOING TO STAY FOR AN EXTRA WEEK, AND TO GREET EVERYONE BACK HERE...

HE WROTE TO YOU, BUT HE DIDN'T WRITE TO ME! THAT BLOCKHEAD!

LET'S HUSTLE A LITTLE MORE ON THOSE FLY-BALLS!

C'MON! MOVE IN ON THOSE GROUNDERS! THROW THE BALL! DON'T HANG ON TO IT!

ALL RIGHT! EVERYBODY OVER HERE ON THE DOUBLE! LET'S GO!

OKAY, TEAM, THIS IS THE START OF A NEW SEASON, AND I HAVE A FEW WORDS TO SAY..

NOW, I THINK NO ONE WILL DENY THAT SPIRIT PLAYS AN IMPORTANT ROLE IN WINNING BALL GAMES..

SOME MIGHT SAY THAT IT PLAYS THE MOST IMPORTANT ROLE..

THE DESIRE TO WIN IS WHAT MAKES A TEAM GREAT..WINNING IS EVERYTHING!

THE ONLY THING THAT MATTERS IS TO COME IN FIRST PLACE!

WHAT I'M TRYING TO SAY IS THAT NO ONE EVER REMEMBERS WHO COMES IN SECOND PLACE!

I DO, CHARLIE BROWN... IN 1928, THE GIANTS AND PHILADELPHIA FINISHED SECOND.. IN 1929, IT WAS PITTSBURGH AND THE YANKEES..IN 1930, IT WAS CHICAGO AND WASHINGTON..IN 1931, IT WAS THE GIANTS AND THE YANKEES..IN 1932, IT WAS PITTSBURGH AND...

AND ANOTHER GREAT SEASON GETS UNDERWAY!

SCHULZ

I DON'T KNOW ABOUT THIS NEXT BATTER, CHARLIE BROWN..HE'S PRETTY GOOD..

THAT'S RIGHT, CHARLIE BROWN.. YOU'D BETTER WATCH HIM..

WELL, WHAT DO YOU THINK? SHALL I GIVE HIM THE OL' CHANGE OF PACE? THE LET-UP?

NO, HE'D KILL IT, CHARLIE BROWN...JUST GIVE HIM FAST ONES, BUT KEEP THEM LOW..

LINUS IS RIGHT, CHARLIE BROWN..

OKAY..FAST BALLS IT IS... LET'S GET 'IM !

WHAT WOULD HE DO IF WE EVER STARTED PLAYING **NIGHT** GAMES?

WELL, I GUESS I'M THE NEXT HITTER...

KEEP THE TRADEMARK UP, LUCY, AND THERE'LL BE LESS CHANCE OF CRACKING THE BAT..

OKAY, MANAGER.. ANYTHING YOU SAY!

STRIKE ONE!

STRIKE TWO!

STRIKE THREE!

YOU WERE RIGHT, MANAGER.. I KEPT THE TRADEMARK UP, AND I DIDN'T CRACK THE BAT!

MY STOMACH HURTS..

TIME OUT!

I JUST THOUGHT OF SOMETHING.. TODAY IS MOTHER'S DAY..

I KNOW IT IS

WHAT DID HE SAY? I THOUGHT I HEARD SCHROEDER MENTION MOTHER'S DAY...

TODAY IS MOTHER'S DAY.. WE'RE PLAYING BASEBALL ON MOTHER'S DAY!

WE SHOULD BE HOME SERVING OUR MOTHERS BREAKFAST IN BED!

MY MOTHER IS ALWAYS DOING NICE THINGS FOR ME

EVERY TIME MY MOTHER GOES TO THE STORE SHE BRINGS ME A SURPRISE

MY MOTHER ALWAYS SINGS TO ME BEFORE I GO TO SLEEP AT NIGHT

HOW CAN WE BE SO SELFISH AS TO SPEND THIS DAY AWAY FROM HOME?

WE'RE CRUEL AND HEARTLESS!

WE HAVE NO SHAME!

WE'RE NO GOOD!

WE NEVER THINK OF ANYONE BUT OURSELVES!

WAAAAHH!!

WE'RE NO GOOD! WE'RE THOUGHTLESS! WE'RE SELFISH AND CRUEL AND...

ACTUALLY, I SENT MY MOTHER A VERY NICE CARD AND A DOZEN PINK ROSES..

GOOD GRIEF! ANOTHER HOME RUN!

BOY, I MUST BE STUPID TO STAND OUT HERE, AND TAKE A BEATING LIKE THIS!

MY TEAM HATES ME, I'M A LOUSY PITCHER, MY STOMACH HURTS..... I DON'T KNOW WHY I PLAY THIS GAME..I MUST REALLY BE STUPID!

CHARLIE BROWN, YOU CAN'T GO ON LIKE THIS..YOU'VE GOT TO CHANGE YOUR ATTITUDE! THE YEARS ARE GOING BY, AND YOU'RE NOT ENJOYING LIFE AT ALL!

JUST REMEMBER, CHARLIE BROWN...THE MOMENTS YOU SPEND OUT HERE ON THIS PITCHER'S MOUND ARE MOMENTS TO BE TREASURED!

WE'RE NOT GOING TO BE KIDS FOREVER, CHARLIE BROWN, SO TREASURE THESE MOMENTS...

POW!

THIS IS A DIFFICULT MOMENT TO TREASURE!

THIS GUY SAYS FOR ME TO TELL YOU THAT IF YOU THROW ANYTHING THAT EVEN **LOOKS** LIKE IT MIGHT BE A BEAN-BALL, HE'S GOING TO COME OUT HERE AND POUND YOU RIGHT INTO THE GROUND!

POW!

POW!

POW!

I THINK THEY'RE BEGINNING TO
GET TO ME... I NEED A NEW PITCH
OR SOMETHING...WHAT DO YOU
THINK I NEED, SCHROEDER?

A CONCRETE PILLBOX!

Schulz

OW!
WHAT HAPPENED? WHAT'S THE MATTER?

I GOT HIT ON THE FINGER WITH A FOUL TIP...

IS IT GOING TO BE ALL RIGHT? ARE YOU GOING TO BE ABLE TO PLAY?
I'M NOT SURE.....I'LL HAVE TO FIND OUT

IT'S ALL RIGHT...I CAN PLAY!

THAT ISN'T EXACTLY WHAT I MEANT...

HI, ROY... WHO YOU WRITIN' TO?

I'M WRITING TO A LITTLE KID NAMED LINUS THAT I MET AT CAMP SEVERAL WEEKS AGO

IS HE CUTE? IF HE IS, TELL HIM YOUR VERY GOOD FRIEND, "PEPPERMINT" PATTY SAYS, "HELLO"

TELL HIM WHAT A REAL SWINGER I AM...

PUT IN A GOOD WORD FOR ME, ROY, AND THE NEXT TIME WE INDIAN WRESTLE I'LL TRY NOT TO CLOBBER YOU!

YOU SAY YOU MET THIS LINUS KID AT CAMP?

YES, AND THE YEAR BEFORE I MET A FRIEND OF HIS NAMED CHARLIE BROWN..

HE WAS A STRANGE ROUND-HEADED KID WHO NEVER TALKED ABOUT ANYTHING EXCEPT BASEBALL AND THIS AWFUL TEAM OF HIS THAT ALWAYS LOSES...

I LOVE BASEBALL! GET ON THE PHONE, QUICK! TELL HIM YOUR FRIEND, "PEPPERMINT" PATTY, HAS VOLUNTEERED TO HELP!

I REALLY LOVE BASEBALL! I'LL TAKE OVER THIS KID'S TEAM, AND SHOW HIM HOW TO **WIN**!!

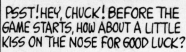

THIS IS RIDICULOUS!

I'VE HIT FIVE HOME RUNS AND PITCHED A NO-HIT GAME, AND WE'RE BEHIND THIRTY-SEVEN TO FIVE! WHOEVER HEARD OF THIRTY-SEVEN UNEARNED RUNS? THIS IS RIDICULOUS!

I THOUGHT I COULD HELP YOUR TEAM, CHUCK, BUT IT'S HOPELESS! I'M GOING BACK WHERE I CAME FROM!

THAT MUST BE A NICE THING TO BE ABLE TO DO...

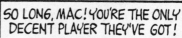

YOU'RE LEAVING?

OF COURSE, I'M LEAVING! I CAN'T HELP **THIS** STUPID TEAM!

SO LONG, MAC! YOU'RE THE ONLY DECENT PLAYER THEY'VE GOT!

HE'S A GOOD PLAYER, BUT I STILL THINK HE'S THE FUNNIEST LOOKING KID I'VE EVER SEEN!

SCHULZ

DEAR PEPPERMINT PATTY, I HOPE YOU HAD A NICE WALK HOME.

I JUST WANTED YOU TO KNOW THAT I APPRECIATED YOUR COMING CLEAR ACROSS TOWN TO HELP OUR TEAM.

SINCERELY,

" CHUCK "

EVERY NIGHT IT'S THE SAME..

I HAVE SUPPER IN MY RED DISH AND DRINKING WATER IN MY YELLOW DISH...

TONIGHT I THINK I'LL HAVE MY SUPPER IN THE YELLOW DISH AND MY DRINKING WATER IN THE RED DISH

LIFE IS TOO SHORT NOT TO LIVE IT UP A LITTLE!

AHEM!

OH, COME NOW! IF YOU'RE TRYING TO TELL ME IT'S SUPPERTIME, YOU'RE WAY OFF!

YOU'RE NOT EVEN **CLOSE** !

YOU MAY THINK IT'S SUPPERTIME, BUT IT ISN'T...

YOUR CLOCK MUST BE WRONG..

THAT'S HARD TO BELIEVE..

IT HAS TO BE SUPPERTIME...

MY STOMACH-CLOCK JUST WENT OFF!

I BROUGHT YOU SOMETHING SPECIAL TONIGHT, SNOOPY...I MIXED IN A FEW TABLE SCRAPS...

TABLE SCRAPS?! WELL, I NEVER!

I REFUSE TO EAT SOMETHING THAT HAS BEEN ON SOMEONE ELSE'S PLATE!

TABLE SCRAPS, INDEED!

IN ALL THE TIME I WAS AT THE DAISY HILL PUPPY FARM, WE NEVER HAD TABLE SCRAPS! NO, SIR! WE HAD GOOD SOLID DOG FOOD!

TABLE SCRAPS! OUTRAGEOUS!!

ALL RIGHT, FORGET THE WHOLE THING.. I'LL SEE YOU TOMORROW..

LET'S NOT BE HASTY! WHAT'S A FEW TABLE SCRAPS AMONG FRIENDS?

SIGH!

RATS!

HE ALWAYS PUTS TOO MUCH CINNAMON ON MY CINNAMON TOAST!

I REFUSE TO CHASE A STICK THAT HASN'T BEEN PROPERLY SANDED AND POLISHED!

BLEAH!

I'VE TAKEN ENOUGH OF YOUR INSULTS! C'MON, YOU AND I ARE GONNA FIGHT!

YOUR SUPPER'S READY, SNOOPY..I SET IT RIGHT OVER THERE IF YOU WANT IT...

C'MON, FORGET ABOUT EATING! FIGHT LIKE A MAN!

NO! I'M NOT GONNA SHAKE HANDS!

IF YOU WANT TO GET OUT OF THIS FIGHT, YOU'RE GOING TO HAVE TO APOLOGIZE BY KISSING MY HAND!

SIGH

I ACCEPT YOUR APOLOGY!

SMACK!

WHAT'S A LITTLE PRIDE WHERE YOUR STOMACH IS CONCERNED?

THIS IS GREAT FOR HIM..HE'LL SIT HERE ALL DAY AS LONG AS I SCRATCH HIS HEAD...

BUT WHAT DO I GET OUT OF IT? A HANDFUL OF TIRED FINGERS, THAT'S WHAT I GET OUT OF IT!

I STAND HERE SCRATCHING AND SCRATCHING AND SCRATCHING..I DO ALL THE WORK WHILE HE JUST SITS THERE..SOMETIMES I THINK HE TAKES ADVANTAGE OF ME

I'LL END UP GETTING TENDINITIS OR SOMETHING, AND HAVE TO GO TO A DOCTOR AND GET A SHOT... I COULD STAND HERE UNTIL BOTH MY ARMS FALL OFF FOR ALL HE CARES... GOOD GRIEF!

I'M THE SORT OF PERSON PEOPLE JUST NATURALLY TAKE ADVANTAGE OF...THAT'S THE TROUBLE WITH THIS WORLD...HALF THE PEOPLE ARE THE KIND WHO TAKE ADVANTAGE OF THE OTHER HALF!

WELL, I'M NOT GOING TO BE THE KIND WHO GETS TAKEN ADVANTAGE OF! I'M NOT GOING TO JUST STAND HERE AND SCRATCH HIS HEAD FOREVER

I REFUSE TO LET SOMEONE TAKE ADVANTAGE OF ME THIS WAY...I'M NOT GOING TO LET HIM DO IT... I MEAN, WHY SHOULD I?

I'M JUST THE SORT OF PERSON PEOPLE NATURALLY TAKE ADVANTAGE OF....

HERE..MOM JUST TOOK SOME OF YOUR SOCKS OUT OF THE DRYER..

SHE SAID FOR YOU TO PUT THEM IN YOUR DRESSER

SECURITY IS HAVING A DRAWER-FULL OF WARM SOCKS!

DO THUMBS EVER SPOIL?

ARE YOU GOING TO HANG ONTO THAT BLANKET FOR THE REST OF YOUR LIFE?

DON'T BE RIDICULOUS..SOMEDAY I'LL JUST TOSS IT AWAY LIKE THAT...

SOMEDAY!

GOOD GRIEF, IT'S STARTING TO RAIN

IN THE BIG LEAGUES WHEN IT STARTS TO RAIN, THE GROUNDSKEEPER COVERS THE PITCHER'S MOUND WITH A TARP

WHAT DO I HAVE TO USE?

HANDKERCHIEFS!

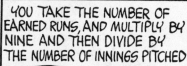

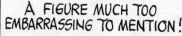

LOOK, THE FIRST OFFICIAL LEAF OF AUTUMN!

LEAVES HAVE BEEN FALLING FOR WEEKS...WHAT MAKES THAT ONE SO OFFICIAL?

I HAD IT NOTARIZED!

SEE THESE LEAVES, LINUS? THEY'RE FLYING SOUTH FOR THE WINTER!

WHAT MAKES YOU THINK THOSE LEAVES ARE FLYING SOUTH, LUCY?

WHEN YOU LOOK AT A MAP, NORTH IS UP AND SOUTH IS DOWN, ISN'T IT? WELL, ISN'T IT?

SEE THESE LEAVES, LINUS? THEY'RE FLYING SOUTH FOR THE WINTER!

NOW, ALL YOU HAVE TO DO IS HOLD THE KITE LIKE THIS, AND THEN LET GO WHEN I TELL YOU TO...

ARE YOU READY?

OKAY, LET GO!!

AAUGHH!

MY KITE! MY BEAUTIFUL KITE! YOU DIDN'T LET GO! I SAID TO LET GO, AND YOU DIDN'T LET GO!

YOU DIDN'T SAY, "PLEASE"

"YEARS FROM NOW WHEN I GET DRAFTED, THE ARMY EXAMINER WILL ASK ME WHY I HAVE THIS KITE WITH ME, AND I'LL SAY, "DON'T ASK SUCH STUPID QUESTIONS""

I CAN'T FIND MY STUPID EYE PATCH!

MY OPHTHALMOLOGIST WILL KILL ME IF I DON'T WEAR THAT EYE PATCH EVERY DAY..

WHERE COULD IT BE?

SAIL HO! LOOK ALIVE, MEN! IT'S THE "QUEEN ANNE'S REVENGE"!

YOU SHOULD HAVE HEARD ME TODAY AT "SHOW AND TELL" TIME

I TOLD THE WHOLE CLASS ALL ABOUT "AMBLYOPIA" AND WHY I WEAR THIS EYE PATCH..I EXPLAINED HOW MY "LAZY EYE" IS BEING STRENGTHENED BY BEING FORCED TO WORK WHILE MY OTHER EYE IS COVERED...

THEN I URGED THEM ALL TO GO SEE THEIR OPHTHALMOLOGISTS FOR EYE TESTS IMMEDIATELY!

DID YOU GET A GOOD GRADE?

I GOT A "B" FROM MY TEACHER AND AN "A" FROM MY OPHTHALMOLOGIST!

FANTASTIC!

HAVE YOU EVER KNOWN ANYONE WHO HAS THE GIFT OF PROPHECY?

JUST MYSELF

YOU?!

ABSOLUTELY! I CAN PREDICT WHAT ANY ADULT WILL ANSWER WHEN HE OR SHE IS ASKED A CERTAIN QUESTION..

IF YOU GO UP TO AN ADULT, AND SAY, "HOW COME WE HAVE A MOTHER'S DAY AND A FATHER'S DAY, BUT WE DON'T HAVE A CHILDREN'S DAY?" THAT ADULT WILL ALWAYS ANSWER, "EVERY DAY IS CHILDREN'S DAY!"

IT DOESN'T MATTER WHAT ADULT YOU ASK... YOU WILL ALWAYS GET THE SAME ANSWER..IT IS AN ABSOLUTE CERTAINTY!

I'LL TRY IT OUT ON GRANDMA..

GRANDMA, HOW COME WE HAVE A MOTHER'S DAY AND A FATHER'S DAY, BUT WE DON'T HAVE A CHILDREN'S DAY?

EVERY DAY IS CHILDREN'S DAY

THE GIFT OF PROPHECY!

YES, MA'AM... I'D LIKE TO BE IN THE SPELLING BEE...

PSST...YOU'RE CRAZY...DON'T DO IT... YOU'LL JUST MAKE A FOOL OUT OF YOURSELF...

I WILL NOT!

EXCUSE ME, MA'AM...I WAS ANSWERING ONE OF MY MANY DETRACTORS...

NOBODY THINKS I CAN WIN THE CITY SPELLING BEE, SNOOPY, BUT I'M GONNA SHOW 'EM!

I NOT ONLY KNOW A LOT OF HARD WORDS, BUT I KNOW EVERY SPELLING RULE IN THE BOOK...

THE ONLY ONE I HAVE TROUBLE REMEMBERING IS, "I BEFORE E EXCEPT AFTER D".....OR IS IT "E BEFORE I EXCEPT AFTER G"?

"I BEFORE B EXCEPT AFTER T"? "V BEFORE Z EXCEPT AFTER E"?

GOOD GRIEF!

WELL, HERE I AM IN THE FIRST ROUND OF THE SPELLING BEE..

I'VE GOT TO STAY CALM AND NOT GET RATTLED...THIS IS MY BIG CHANCE TO PROVE TO EVERYONE THAT I CAN DO SOMETHING!

I DON'T CARE IF I DON'T ACTUALLY WIN..ALL I WANT IS TO GET PAST THE FIRST FEW ROUNDS, AND MAKE A DECENT SHOWING...LET'S SEE NOW...HOW DOES THAT RULE GO?

"E BEFORE I EXCEPT AFTER G" NO, THAT'S NOT RIGHT.." I BEFORE G EXCEPT AFTER.." NO..."C BEFORE E EXCEPT...EXCEPT."...HMMM....

SCHULZ

I GUESS I REALLY DON'T HAVE TO WORRY..

ALL THE WORDS IN THE FIRST ROUND OF A SPELLING BEE USUALLY ARE QUITE EASY... THAT KID SURE GOT AN EASY ONE...

IN A WAY, I'D ALMOST LIKE TO START OFF WITH A HARD ONE.. YOU KNOW, TO KIND OF SHAKE UP THE OTHER KIDS...TO SORT OF LET THEM SEE WHO THEY'RE UP AGAINST

I FEEL STRANGELY CALM..

SCHULZ

YES, MA'AM? ME? WHY DID I HAVE MY HEAD ON MY DESK? YOU DON'T KNOW? YOU'RE ASKING ME WHY I HAD MY HEAD ON MY DESK?

BECAUSE I BLEW THE STUPID SPELLING BEE, THAT'S WHY!!!

OH, GOOD GRIEF! NOW, I'VE DONE IT!

"PLEAD MY CAUSE, O LORD, WITH THEM THAT STRIVE WITH ME: FIGHT AGAINST THEM THAT FIGHT AGAINST ME...DELIVER ME FROM THE HAND OF THEM THAT PERSECUTE ME.."

OFFICE of the PRINCIPAL

MY STOMACH HURTS!

OFFICE of the PRINCIPAL

EXCUSE ME...I'M SUPPOSED TO SEE THE PRINCIPAL..

WHAT ABOUT? WELL, MY TEACHER SENT ME IN...I GUESS I YELLED AT HER..

I DIDN'T MEAN TO YELL AT HER...I WAS SORT OF UPSET AT THE TIME, AND...WELL...

NOW I'M SUPPOSED TO SEE THE PRINCIPAL..

SO HERE I AM IN THE PRINCIPAL'S OFFICE...GOOD GRIEF!

THIS NEVER WOULD HAVE HAPPENED IF I HADN'T GOOFED UP THAT STUPID SPELLING BEE..

WHEN THE TEACHER SAID FOR ME TO SPELL "MAZE," THE FIRST THING THAT CAME TO MY MIND WAS WILLIE MAYS.....OH, WELL...

MAYBE SOMEDAY AFTER I'M GROWN UP, I'LL MEET WILLIE MAYS, AND I'LL TELL HIM WHAT HAPPENED, AND WE'LL HAVE A GOOD LAUGH TOGETHER

YES, SIR...I WAS TOLD BY MY TEACHER TO COME TO YOUR OFFICE...

NO, I'VE NEVER BEEN HERE BEFORE.. I'VE NEVER DONE ANYTHING REALLY WRONG BEFORE......

YOU HAVE A NICE OFFICE..

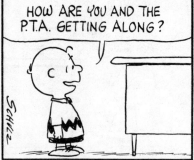

HOW ARE YOU AND THE P.T.A. GETTING ALONG?

NO, SIR, I DON'T THINK IT WAS RIGHT TO YELL AT MRS. DONOVAN, MY TEACHER..

WHAT DO I THINK MY FATHER WILL SAY?!

WELL, SIR, HE'S A VERY UNDERSTANDING PERSON...I REALLY THINK THAT WHEN I EXPLAIN THE WHOLE STORY, HE'LL UNDERSTAND...HE WON'T CONDEMN ME...

HE'S LEARNED A LOT ABOUT PEOPLE IN HIS BARBER SHOP, AND HE KNOWS HOW THINGS SOMETIMES JUST SORT OF HAPPEN...SO I DON'T THINK HE'LL SAY MUCH...MOM IS THE SAME WAY...

I DO HAVE A FEW FRIENDS, HOWEVER, WHO MIGHT HAVE SOME THOUGHTS ON THE SUBJECT!

THE TITLE OF MY THEME IS, "EXPERIENCES AT SUMMER CAMP"

"AS I GOT OFF THE CAMP BUS THAT DAY, I SENSED THAT THE WOODS WERE FULL OF QUEEN SNAKES! QUEEN SNAKES TO THE LEFT OF ME.... QUEEN SNAKES TO THE RIGHT OF ME... QUEEN SNAKES ALL AROUND ME! I.."

KLUNK !

POOR MISS OTHMAR... I KEEP FORGETTING SHE HAS A THING ABOUT QUEEN SNAKES!

YOU THINK BEETHOVEN WAS GREAT...

WELL, WHAT ABOUT CHOPIN, BACH, MOZART, BLOCH, BARTOK, BERLIOZ, BIZET, BRAHMS, DELIUS, DEBUSSY AND DVORAK?

WHAT ABOUT ELGAR, FRANCK, GLINKA, GRIEG, HANDEL, HAYDN, HUMPERDINCK, LISZT, MAHLER, MENDELSSOHN, RAVEL, RACHMANINOFF, SCHUBERT, SIBELIUS, TSCHAIKOWSKY AND VIVALDI?

THEY WERE GREAT, TOO..

RATS! FOR ONE BRIEF MOMENT I THOUGHT I HAD HIM!

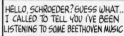

HELLO, SCHROEDER? GUESS WHAT... I CALLED TO TELL YOU I'VE BEEN LISTENING TO SOME BEETHOVEN MUSIC

I'VE ALSO BEEN READING HIS BIOGRAPHY...IT'S VERY INTERESTING.. SORT OF SAD, AND YET SORT OF INSPIRING...YOU KNOW WHAT I MEAN?

I HAVE A POST CARD, TOO, THAT I THINK YOU'D LIKE...AN UNCLE OF MINE SENT IT TO ME FROM BONN, GERMANY...THEY HAVE A MUSEUM THERE

I GUESS THAT'S WHERE BEETHOVEN WAS BORN, ISN'T IT? I'LL BET YOU'D ENJOY VISITING THERE.. MAYBE YOU'LL HAVE A CHANCE TO SOMEDAY...

ANYWAY, THAT'S WHY I CALLED BECAUSE I KNEW YOU'D BE INTERESTED, AND I JUST WANTED TO TELL YOU ABOUT THESE THINGS...

IT'S NOT PROPER FOR A GIRL TO CALL A BOY ON THE TELEPHONE

AAUGH!!

SCHULZ

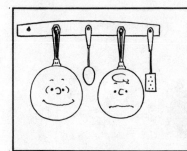

WHAT IF YOU AND I GOT MARRIED SOMEDAY, SCHROEDER?

AND WHAT IF WE WERE SO POOR YOU HAD TO SELL YOUR PIANO SO WE COULD BUY SAUCEPANS?

SAUCEPANS?

SURE, YOU WOULDN'T EXPECT ME TO KEEP HOUSE WITHOUT A GOOD SET OF SAUCEPANS, WOULD YOU?

SAUCEPANS?!

GIRLS HAVE TO THINK ABOUT THESE THINGS.. BOYS ARE LUCKY...THEY NEVER HAVE TO WORRY ABOUT THINGS LIKE SAUCEPANS...

I CAN'T STAND IT...I JUST CAN'T STAND IT...

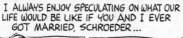

IF DECEMBER TWELFTH IS HERE, CAN BEETHOVEN'S BIRTHDAY BE FAR AWAY?

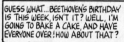

GUESS WHAT...BEETHOVEN'S BIRTHDAY IS THIS WEEK, ISN'T IT? WELL, I'M GOING TO BAKE A CAKE, AND HAVE EVERYONE OVER! HOW ABOUT THAT?

I THINK SUCH AN EFFORT ON MY PART DESERVES A REWARD, DON'T YOU? LIKE MAYBE A LITTLE KISS...

I MEAN, AFTER ALL, SOMEONE LIKE YOURSELF WHO ADMIRES BEETHOVEN SO MUCH SHOULD BE WILLING TO REWARD A PERSON WHO WORKS HARD TO...

SMACK

AAUGH! I'VE BEEN KISSED BY A DOG!!

I'VE BEEN POISONED! GET SOME IODINE! GET SOME HOT WATER! GERMS! GERMS! GERMS!

HAPPY BEETHOVEN'S BIRTHDAY....THURSDAY!

I'D GIVE ANYTHING TO BE ABLE TO TALK WITH THAT LITTLE RED-HAIRED GIRL..

THE AMAZING THING IS THAT I **KNOW** I'M THE SORT OF PERSON SHE'D LIKE! I MEAN I'M NOT ROUGH OR CRUDE OR ANYTHING

I'M NOT THE GREATEST PERSON WHO EVER LIVED, OF COURSE, BUT AFTER ALL, WHO IS? I'M JUST A NICE SORT OF GUY WHO....

..WHO NEVER GETS TO MEET LITTLE RED-HAIRED GIRLS!

WHAT'S THIS? THAT LITTLE RED-HAIRED GIRL DROPPED HER PENCIL...

GEE...IT'S GOT TEETH MARKS ALL OVER IT...

SHE NIBBLES ON HER PENCIL...

SHE'S HUMAN!

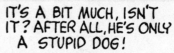

HEY! ZIP!

WHAT DO YOU THINK YOU'RE DOING? NO FUTURE HUSBAND OF MINE IS GOING TO SIT AROUND HOLDING A BLANKET!

I'M NOT YOUR FUTURE HUSBAND! GIVE ME THAT BLANKET! NO!

MY BLANKET! I GOTTA HAVE THAT BLANKET! I CAN'T BREATHE! I FEEL DIZZY... I'M GROWING FAINT...I...I...

OHHHHHH GET UP! I KNOW YOU'RE FAKING!

GIMME THAT BLANKET, OR I'LL CLOBBER YOU! I WON'T GIVE IT BACK UNLESS YOU PROMISE TO MARRY ME...

ALL RIGHT, I PROMISE TO MARRY YOU! YOU DO???

YOU'RE LYING!!!! WHAP!

JUST THINK...IF WE WERE MARRIED, YOU WOULDN'T NEED A BLANKET BECAUSE JUST KNOWING I WAS THERE IN OUR LITTLE HOME WOULD MAKE YOU FEEL SO SECURE.... I CAN'T STAND IT...

SCHULZ

 I LIKE YOU, LINUS... I LIKE YOU, AND I ADMIRE YOU, BUT I COULD LIKE YOU EVEN MORE IF YOU'D GIVE UP THAT BLANKET...

 I DON'T REALLY CARE IF YOU LIKE ME OR NOT...

 I LOOK FORWARD TO THE DAY WHEN I'LL UNDERSTAND GIRLS..

HEY!

LOOK AT THAT, WILL YOU?

WHAT'S THE MATTER?

THAT BIG KID JUST PUSHED DOWN THAT LITTLE RED-HAIRED GIRL! WHAT A BULLY!

SHE GOT UP....BUT, LOOK! HE'S GOING TO PUSH HER DOWN AGAIN!

OH, WHY AREN'T I TOUGH? WHY CAN'T I RUSH OVER THERE AND SAVE HER?

BECAUSE I'D GET SLAUGHTERED, THAT'S WHY! I'M NOT TOUGH... I'M NOT ANYTHING! I'M...

CRACK!

I'LL TAKE CARE OF HIM, CHARLIE BROWN!

CRACK!

YOU CAN RELAX, CHARLIE BROWN...HE WON'T BOTHER HER ANY MORE!

THAT'S VERY COMFORTING... I'M THE FRIEND OF A HERO!